McGrew and the BIG Zyme MEET

Written & Illustrated by Rachel Ruth

Endorsements

"Enzymes are not just important to life and health, but are absolutely essential for both. It is curious that enzymes are the most studied phenomenon of medical science, yet sadly, enzymes are one of the least discussed and explained issues by the health care community.

If the general population were taught the basics of enzymes, far less pain, disease and suffering would be experienced by the average person, never mind the amount of money that would be saved on medical expense.

In *McGrew and the Big Zyme Meet*, by Rachel Ruth, the concept of enzymes and their relevance to our health is entertainingly explained for young readers (and their parents who read this work to them.)

Many children suffer needlessly from numerous infections and other ailments simply for a lack of knowledge about the importance of live foods (enzymatically alive) vs. processed foods (dead foods), which this book covers.

While *McGrew and the Big Zyme Meet* is not a manual of health as such, the principles contained herein, can literally change the life and health for the betterment of all who apply its truths."

— Dr. Joel R. Robbins

"Very impressive in presentation of story, idea, art and education.
A great book for the whole family."
— *Steve McBride, Advertising Director, Independence Daily Reporter, Independence, KS*

"The book presents a simple yet powerful message. Vibrant colors show how living foods should look. I was captivated by the Zymes' energy and life-giving abilities."
— *Lori Dale (mother of 4)*

"I think it's a fun way to educate. I heard of enzymes,
but never gave it much thought. Now, I actually understand their function.
It gives me purpose to change the way I eat."
— *Denise Breheny*

"This is a breathtakingly beautiful book for students to learn in a very motivational way how important fresh foods are (to their bodies now and in the future!)"
— *Mary Conn (English teacher)*

"*McGrew and the Big Zyme Meet* by Rachel Ruth is a gift from the heart.
Just as Dr. Seuss books were the rage of another generation and still remain a part of every child's library, I predict that Rachel Ruth's rhythms and Zymes
will rap themselves into our hearts, forever!"
— *Donna M. Rothgeb (retired teacher)*

"I like it! Can you read it again?"
— *Annalise Dale (5 years)*

To my dear family,
friends,
and professional nutritionists
who inspired me,
advised me,
and encouraged me to
see my passion become a real tool,
helping others everywhere
become healthier and happier...
thank you from the bottom of my heart!

This book is full of surprises
and is waiting for you
to open it and discover the treasures inside.
May the Divine Designer inspire you
as you read it,
hopefully changing your life forever!

Once upon a time

in the land of Eaton

lived a wise little man

named McGrew.

He surfed the net till his eyes
turned pink,
and he thought that he
was through...

when...

all of a sudden before his eyes
came a GREAT BIG BANNER
(to his surprise,) announcing...
ZYME MEETING! LAND OF EATON!
NOW!

Why, that was

right next door!

McGrew grabbed his

big bag and

flew across the floor!

He opened the gate, stepped up to the door. McGrew knocked only twice, not any more.

The door opened quickly and all over the place McGrew saw Zymes by the thousands, every color and race!

There were "Tree" Zymes, "Vine" Zymes,
"Bush" Zymes, and more.
They were happy and dancing, all over the floor.

Their joyful chants and melodies ringing made McGrew happy, too, so he joined in their singing!

Rachel
© 2004

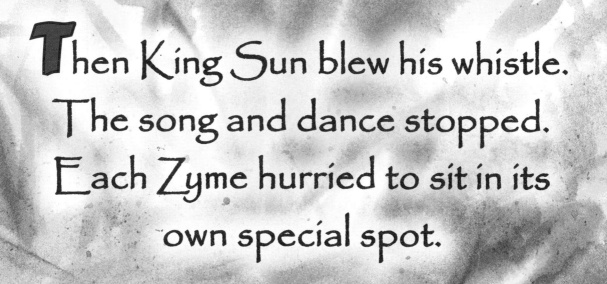

Then King Sun blew his whistle.
The song and dance stopped.
Each Zyme hurried to sit in its
own special spot.

"You all are so awesome
I welcome you here
There's a big
job to do
in this
coming-up
year!"

said the king of each Zyme
in his very best rhyme.

"**M**any people are sick,
unhappy, with flu.
They're full of diseases, and they
ALL need YOU!"

Rachel
© 2004

"I'm sending you, LIFE GIVERS, OUT TO THE CROWD!

Go to the people everywhere," King Sun said aloud.

Rachel © 2004

"You will help everyone,

not just the sick;

the rule

is important.

You've got to be quick!"

King Sun's clock was ticking.
TOCK-TICK... TOCK-TICK...
TOCK-TICK!

Each Zyme was so quiet,
leaning up in his seat.
Stillness was important at this
GIANT Zyme meet!

The Sun King spoke clearly so every Zyme heard, "The rule means everything!" (Shh...they missed not a word.)

"You're active!

You're healthy!

You can sing!

You can see!

The food you're

attached to

is life's energy."

"Babies and children,
moms, dads, grandparents, too,
are all needing help!
They'll be coming to you!"

"You'll go to the people in schools and in homes. Accept it. Your mission: give health to their bones."

The Sun King continued,
his face all aglow,

"My SUN strength will be with you!
Help the people to grow!"

Rachel ©2004

"Help them grow to be healthy, have birthdays, play sports!
This world should be singing happy words of all sorts...like

'Howdy!' 'Glad to see you!'
'My, you're looking fine!'
'Your children are so healthy!'
'So are mine.'

          '...and mine!'

               '...and mine!'"

Rachel © 2004

"Your time has now come.
Don't delay any more!
Cling to those fresh foods
that go to the store."

"This meeting is over!
I love you so much!
My Zymes, you are special!
Many lives you will touch!"

So Zymes were sent out by the
Sun King that day...
to gardens, farms, orchards,
and stores like Foodway.

Rachel © 2004

They jumped into broccoli, watermelon and beans... celery, spinach, and lettuce and everything green.

Peaches, apples on trees, and grapes on the vines were filled just like carrots with life-giving Zymes!

Here's Kevin and Bubbie, Auntie and Pap!
They're dancing and happy and chanting a rap!

Please join them. Start hummin' and jump to your feet...'cause this rap is toe tappin'! You can't miss a beat!

The crowd will sing with you!

It's easy.

It rhymes.

Start clapping together!

Support all those Zymes!

To cook a Zyme would be a crime!

There's health right now for YOU!

Gotta sing. Gotta dance.

Don't be sick...not a chance!

Tell your friends that this is true.

So clap your hands,

clap-clap, clap-clap

and stomp your feet,

tap-tap, tap-tap.

Help Zymes tell the world:

(Clap-clap Tap-tap!)

MORE RAW FOOD EAT!

RAW-RAW FOOD EAT!!

RAW-RAW FOOD EAT!!!

So What's a Zyme?

I'm so glad you asked! First of all, "zyme" is short for "enzyme." Enzymes are the primary reason for eating a raw food diet! All raw, alive foods have an abundance of enzymes, the secret to life, the key to understanding proper nutrition. Our bodies were designed to receive food with enzymes.

The enzymes in our bodies work with the raw food enzymes to digest our food. All food that is alive in its raw state has the necessary enzymes within itself to break itself down.

It is useless to calculate a food's nutritional value based on its vitamins, minerals, carbohydrates, proteins, or fats…if the food has been cooked. Heating foods above 105-118 degrees destroys all the enzymes in them.

When you eat cooked foods that no longer have their enzymes intact, your body is forced to compensate by expending energy for digestion. This creates stress on the pancreas (the main organ in the body that produces digestive enzymes) which can lead to disease and premature aging.

More information about enzymes may be found in the following books:

Enzyme Nutrition by Edward Howell, Avery Publishing Group
Food Enzymes by Tonita d'Raye, Awieca Publishing, Inc.
God's Way to Ultimate Health by Dr. George Malkmus,
　　Hallelujah Acres Publishing
Living on Live Food by Alissa Cohen, Cohen Publishing Co.
Raw Kids by Cheryle Stoycoff, Living Spirit Press
The Enzyme Cure by Lita Lee, Future Medicine Publishing

Raw Recipes to Get You Going
Remember...all ingredients are raw...
(NOT canned or pasteurized!)

Rainbow Nutty Treat

1 apple (cut into small pieces)
1 orange (cut into small pieces)
½ cup strawberries sliced
1 banana sliced
1 kiwi sliced
1 handful blueberries
1 small bunch grapes
1 Tablespoon honey
¼ cup chopped nuts (no peanuts)
Stir in a bowl and enjoy! Serves 2.

Green Shreek Smoothie

3 cups cold watermelon (cut into small pieces)
(Blend this first until it becomes liquid.)
2 cups Romaine lettuce (break leaves into small pieces)
(Blend lettuce into liquid a little at a time.)
**When all is smooth together, pour over ice,
into cups and share! Very, very good!!!**
YUM!

What Did You Learn?

1. What is a Zyme?

2. How many live foods have Zymes in them?

3. How do Zymes help you?

4. What happens to Zymes when they are cooked?

5. How is the Sun important in helping the Zymes?

6. What foods contain Zymes?

7. Why are Zymes happy?

8. What change did you see in McGrew as the story developed?

9. Who can be helped by following McGrew's example?

10. Have you tried any of the recipes?

11. Where can you find food with Zymes?

12. What is "raw" food?

Let this be a

"new beginning"

for you!

Soon you'll be

helping others

to be healthier, too!

Much love, health, and happiness,

Rachel Ruth